Some Birds and Mammals of the Field and Hedgerow

by Kenneth Lilly

THE MEDICI SOCIETY LTD

LONDON 1980

D0300048

Pheasant *(Phasianus colchicus)* PHEASANT FAMILY

Size: Overall length of male 30–35 in (76–89 cm). The long tail feathers may account for up to 20 in (50 cm). The female measures 21–25 in (53–63 cm) including a more modest tail of about 10 in (25 cm).

The cock bird weighs approximately $3\frac{1}{2}$ lb (1.6 kg) and the hen $2\frac{1}{2}$ lb (1.1 kg).

Breeding: There is only one brood a year. The nest is sited in long grass, under brambles or ferns and is nothing more than a scrape carelessly lined with grass and leaves.

Eight to fifteen olive coloured eggs will be laid over a period of about three weeks beginning in April, sometimes later. Once all the eggs are laid, the hen will begin incubation which will take a further 24 days. Her plumage blends so perfectly with her background that even a fox, passing within a few feet of the nest, may not see her.

The hen is in sole charge of rearing the family. The little chicks will be fully active and feeding themselves within a few hours of hatching. They are able to fly when about two weeks old.

At first, the chicks feed almost entirely on insects but slowly change to the more varied diet of the adult bird . . . seeds, berries, acorns, young shoots, grass, insects, worms and the occasional lizard and field vole.

Habits: The pheasant, a native of Asia, was probably introduced into this country by the Romans. Since then, it has become an established and favourite game bird.

Although the harsh cry of the cock bird 'karrk-karrk' can be clearly heard from afar across the fields, the pheasant is a shy, cautious bird and quickly seeks cover when disturbed.

A heavy and largely ground dwelling bird, it takes to flight only as a last resort. It leaps into flight with a flurry of flapping wings and loose downy feathers and rises just high enough for it to glide as far as possible before landing at a safe distance.

In winter, cock and hen pheasants often keep together in mixed groups. Come spring, the males disperse and establish their own territories. They strut, splendidly coloured, proud and ready to accept any challenge made by a rival cock bird.

One magnificent cock bird which regularly feeds in my garden, challenged Tom cat to a territorial 'duel'. Tom however, lounging comfortably on the lawn, studiously ignored him. Thoroughly disgusted by lack of response he strutted off to seek a more worthy opponent.

Rabbit *(Oryctolagus cuniculus)* RABBIT FAMILY

Size: About 16 in (40 cm) long. Weight 3–4 lb (1.5–2 kg). The female, or doe, is usually slightly smaller than the male, or buck.

Breeding: Two or three litters are born each year, usually between January and June. However, young rabbits may be seen at any time of the year, even in snow.

Two to eight babies are born in a litter. They are born blind, deaf and hairless in a burrow. The nursery chamber is dug about two feet long and usually away from the main burrow, or 'warren'. The nest is made of moss, dry leaves and grass, lined with soft grey fur which the doe pulls from her own chest.

The doe visits her babies only once a day to feed them. After each visit, she covers the entrance with earth and grass to hide her nursery from the many hedgerow hunters and other rabbits which might harm them. Their eyes open on the eleventh day. When 14 days old, they may be seen playing outside, though never far from the entrance. At a month old they join the 'grown-ups' in the warren.

Habits: The warren is a network of connecting underground tunnels dug by the rabbits themselves. Here they live in groups. Occasionally, as many as a hundred or more rabbits may be found living together. Rabbits feed mainly at dawn and dusk. They eat grass, shoots and herbs. Tree bark, snails and worms are also eaten when other food is not available.

The rabbit has many enemies and is ever watchful: on the ground for the fox or any member of the weasel family and for large birds of prey from the sky above. When alarmed, the rabbit will thump the ground with both hind feet to alert other rabbits. When in an emergency, it flees for its safety – the white fluffy tail acts as a visual warning.

Well versed in the art of self-preservation, the rabbit sometimes simply out-wits even the wily old fox . . . one evening, I watched a fox searching for its supper. It approached a large bramble patch. As the fox disappeared into one side of the brambles, a rabbit casually hopped out from the other side. It sat down a safe

distance away to wait patiently for the fox to finish exploring the culinary possibilities of the bramble patch. Shortly, the fox re-appeared and continued on its way. The rabbit then casually hopped back into the bramble patch.

Robin (*Erithacus rubecula*) THRUSH FAMILY

Size: $5\frac{1}{2}$ in (14 cm). The male and female are alike.

Breeding: The eccentric nesting habits of the robin are well known. It will build its nest in anything – an old coat pocket, a tin can or a kettle or even in your living room if it can get in. I have had to out-wit more than one robin who has tried to 'move in'. However, it will sometimes settle for a more conventional site in a hedgerow or tree.

The young robin's speckled coat changes to adult plumage in July or August.

The hen may build her nest as early as February, well constructed with grass, dead leaves, moss, hair and feathers. It is usually well disguised and easily overlooked.

Normally, four to six eggs are laid. They are white, speckled with reddish brown although some are whitish pink with few or no markings. The hen will sit on the eggs 13–14 days. During this period, the male will sometimes bring her food. Both parents feed the young, which fly when they are about two weeks old. Two or three families may be reared each year.

Habits: The pert, friendly manner of the robin and its bright red breast, which decorate so many of our Christmas cards has undoubtedly made it a firm favourite with most of us. Friendly though it may be with human beings, especially when they are digging and there is a chance of a worm to eat, it is, however, extremely aggressive towards other birds.

Any bird venturing too close may well find itself confronted by an irate little robin with puffed-out breast feathers and be loudly and soundly scolded. Even other robins are driven from its personal territory outside the breeding season.

During the breeding season however, a male and female will join territories and defend them together. As soon as their young offspring are able to fend for themselves, they too are compelled, often forcibly, to go and seek a territory of their own. By August or September, the adults will resume their own original territories.

The robin, sometimes known as 'Redbreast' as well as having traditional associations with the festive season, has been the object of superstition for centuries. Interfering with its nest or harming the bird in any way is still thought by many folk to bring bad luck and dire consequencies.

Supernatural powers apart, it does possess the

remarkable ability to change its shape. At times, adopting a long-legged, slim, elegant, warbler-like shape and then, suddenly, fluffing out its feathers to resemble something like a furry tennis ball. It will do this regardless of temperature or time of year.

The robin, whilst excitedly flicking its wings and tail, prefers to feed mainly on the ground, seldom far from cover. It tends to favour places with dense undergrowth and, like the wren, may be mistaken for a mouse as it searches among the leaves, weeds and roots for a tasty tit-bit.

The robin's choice of food is as unpredictable as its choice of nesting place. It will dine on scraps, crumbs, nuts, fruit, fat – indeed almost anything is considered edible. It does, however, appear to have a special fondness for insects and worms.

Robin adopting a warbler-like shape.

Harvest Mouse
(*Micromys minutus*)
RODENT FAMILY

Size: Length, including tail about $4\frac{1}{2}$ in (11 cm) weighing no more than $\frac{1}{4}$ oz (7 g).

Breeding: Four to nine babies are born in a litter and the female can produce several litters a year, between April and September.

The nest is constructed from grasses woven into a ball about 3 in (8 cm) across and built around the stems of corn, grass or thistles, 6–18 in (15–46 cm) above the ground. There is no definite entrance but the whole structure is loosely woven and the mice simply push their way through wherever they choose.

Only the female and her babies use the nest. The male doesn't appear to be allowed in.

Habits: This is the smallest mouse found in Britain. It can perch with ease on an ear of wheat without so much as even slightly bending the stem. Its rounded ears and blunt nose are

more vole-like than its cousins', the wood and house mice.

The harvest mouse is undoubtedly the acrobat of the mouse family. Its waking hours are spent climbing precariously up among the stems of grass and corn, tightroping along slender stems, waving its tail from side to side in the manner of a circus 'high-wire' performer with a balancing pole. The moment it stops, it wraps its tail around the nearest support, and, gripping with both hind feet, can thus have both fore feet free for holding its food.

Contrary to its name, the harvest mouse is found in a wide variety of habitats, ranging from corn fields and hedgerows to ditches, dykes, salt marshes and reedbeds. In winter, it leaves the more exposed habitats for the warmer sheltered dense undergrowth of ditches and hedgerows. Here it makes a home in a warm, cosy burrow.

The harvest mouse doesn't really hibernate during winter but does enjoy the occasional prolonged snooze. On waking, it always feels hungry and therefore never sleeps far from its source of food which consists of most seasonally available seeds and insects. The seeds are often stored in a burrow for winter use.

Mice are usually more active at night and, therefore, the frequent sightings of the harvest mouse during the day have mystified many observers. However, recent studies by several naturalists have shown that the harvest mouse lives in a three hourly cycle. Two and a half hours of sleep followed by about half an hour of feeding and so on round the clock. This manner of sleeping and eating throughout the day and night, naturally enough, exposes it to more predators than other mice and may well account to some extent for its scarcity. The chief reason for its decline, though, is probably due to modern farming methods.

Long before the days of selective weed-killers and the devastation of the hedgerows, when the corn was being cut the stubble simply teemed with harvest mice. As children, we played a game of cupping our hands to see who could catch the most mice in one go! These delightful little creatures seemed quite happy to join in the fun.

Its overall numbers have never been thought of as plentiful, but hopefully, being such a tiny creature and not easily seen, it may be with us in much greater numbers than we are aware of.

It is found chiefly in the southern counties of England, rarely in Scotland and never in Ireland.

Mistle Thrush *(Turdus viscivorus)* THRUSH FAMILY

Size: The male and female are alike, both being about 10½ in long (27 cm) and weighing about 4 oz (112 g).

Breeding: The mistle thrush is a bird that seems to prefer a rather private life during the breeding season. It is a shy bird and always difficult to approach at any time but never more so than during this period. Although the mistle thrush is quite a familiar sight in our fields, it usually prefers to build its nest and rear its family in more wooded places. Nevertheless, it will occasionally nest in the hedgerow if a suitable tallish tree can be found. The nest is often built in the fork of a tree or, sometimes, out on a branch, high above the ground. It is built by the female, the male seldom being involved in this part of family life. The nest is constructed from grasses, moss and leaves. This is then strengthened by adding earth and rotten wood and, to add a final touch of luxury, a lining is made from lichens, wool, feathers and down.

Two families are usually reared each year, often from the same nest. The first brood can be as early as the end of February whilst the second is seldom later than April. Each brood consists of two to six eggs. These will vary in colour from pale buff to greenish blue and partially or wholly flecked with dark reddish brown. The hen will sit on the eggs for 14 days. When the eggs hatch, the male will then join the hen to help with feeding the babies.

Although the mistle is by nature a rather shy bird, it will defend its young quite fearlessly. Its method of discouraging intruders is to repeatedly 'dive-bomb' them at high speed. Occasionally, however, it has been known to attack physically such formidable creatures as hawks, crows, squirrels, cats and even men!

Habits: The thrush family have the most musical voices to be heard among British birds. The mistle thrush delights in its beautiful voice and will sing its accompaniment to fair weather or foul. Country folk know it as the 'Stormcock' for it will sit high up on a swinging wind-swept bough, singing its powerful song at the wind.

The Old English name for this large, handsome thrush is 'Mistletoe' thrush because of its liking for mistletoe berries. It will, of course, readily eat other berries and fruit which it finds in the fields and hedgerows.

Oddly enough, for a bird with a liking for tall trees, the mistle thrush spends much of its time on the ground. With an upright stance, it wades tummy deep through grass and under-

growth searching for food, stopping every now and then with head tilted on one side to listen and then, diving suddenly, it will come up with a snail, insect, worm or spider in its bill. Little will escape this very alert, bright-eyed bird.

Outside the breeding season, the mistle thrush prefers pasture land and ploughed fields where, in autumn, it can be seen in small groups and sometimes in quite large flocks or in the company of other members of the thrush family.

The mistle thrush flies with rapid wing beats, regularly closing its wings in a short glide. In flight, it can be recognised by the whitish edge of the outer tail feathers.

Goldfinch
(*Carduelis carduelis*)

FINCH FAMILY

Size: Length about 5 in (13 cm). The male and female are alike.

Breeding: Four to six eggs are laid from May onwards. They are whitish and speckled with dark purplish brown.

The eggs are laid in a small nest beautifully made of grass, moss, wool, thistledown, fine roots and indeed almost any fine material. Some nests include string and flowers. It is not known, however, whether this is supposed to serve a purpose or is simply decoration.

The hen builds the nest in the hedgerow or on the outer branches of a tree. The male,

The young goldfinch lacks the splendid head markings of the parents.

12

although usually in attendance, doesn't actually do anything to help. However, he frequently feeds the hen whilst she is sitting on the eggs and shares in the feeding of the babies when they hatch. The young are able to fly when two weeks old. Two or three families, are reared each year.

Habits: The goldfinch is one of the smaller finches found in Britain. It prefers to live mainly in small groups, known as 'charms' of goldfinches. A charm will rove over the countryside in a wonderfully colourful, animated party, twittering loudly and musically whilst busily working their way from one patch of seed heads to another. Their plumage is a splendid patchwork of bright colours, livening up the dullest day!

They feed on various seed heads, clinging onto the plant as their weight slowly bends the stem, quite unconcerned that they often finish feeding upside down.

Their diet also includes insects for which they will occasionally forage on the ground.

Field Vole *(Microtus agrestis)* RODENT FAMILY

Size: Length when fully grown about $5\frac{1}{4}$ in (13 cm) including $1\frac{1}{4}$ in (3 cm) of tail.

Breeding: The male vole has many 'wives' and takes no part whatsoever in the rearing of his 'families'.

The female builds her nest of split grass stems, woven into a ball. This is positioned near one of its covered runs and blends perfectly with the surrounding grass. Sometimes she will choose to build her nest under a log or fallen tree. In this event, the nest is usually more cup-shaped. Some females have been known simply to use an old birds' nest. This would, probably be the disused nest of a ground-nesting bird as the field vole, unlike its cousin the bank vole, is not very keen on climbing.

The first family of three to seven babies can be born as early as February. They are born blind and naked. They grow very quickly and leave 'home' when about two and a half weeks old. The female can produce her first family when she is only six weeks old and go on to produce a family every five or six weeks until about September.

Although an attentive mother, she will run off and leave her babies if disturbed. She will, however, return later and carry them, one by one, to a new nest.

Habits: The field vole or short-tailed vole, as it is sometimes known, has many enemies. It seldom dares to venture out into the open and therefore digs a network of tunnels just below the surface. Above ground, it pushes runways through the tangled stems of grass without disturbing the grass, thus enabling it to move about freely on the surface and to feed without being seen from above. These runways are shared by other voles.

Occasionally, however, I've known the field vole to throw 'caution to the wind' and boldly venture forth to pull up a crocus bulb growing by my garden gate, then drag it back with considerable effort, into its burrow. This, in full view of three pussies who all lurk languidly only a quick dash and a pounce away!

The field vole feeds for two to three hours at a time, with periods of rest in between, by day and by night. Grass is undoubtedly its favourite food but it is also rather partial to bulbs, roots, bark and insects. Food for the winter is collected and stored in a burrow.

Weasel *(Mustela nivalis)* WEASEL FAMILY

Size: Length 8–11 in (20–28 cm) including about 2 in (5 cm) of tail. Weight about 8 oz (225 g). The female is usually smaller than the male.

Breeding: Three to eight baby weasels, or 'kittens', are born in a nest of dry grass, moss and leaves in a hollow tree or hole in a bank. There are usually two families born between March and August. When the kittens are four or five weeks old, they are taught to hunt and fend for themselves by their mother.

Habits: Although the weasel is found in a variety of habitats, sometimes including city suburbs, the country hedgerow is perhaps its favourite haunt. Here, this pencil-slim little hunter seeks out the voles, mice, rats and small birds which form its main diet. Being so slim, it can pursue a mouse down even the smallest hole. An expert climber, it steals eggs and small birds from nests and will readily plunge into a stream in pursuit of a water vole.

Because the weasel's eye level is only about 2 in (5 cm) above the ground, it stops frequently to sit up and peer above the grass and low undergrowth to see where it is going. Fortunately, it doesn't rely on its sight to find its prey but uses its extremely sensitive sense of smell.

Like the fox, the weasel sometimes 'charms' its intended victim. An unsuspecting bird or rabbit watching the weasel chasing its own tail, somersaulting and rolling about, is quite unaware that this seemingly playful little creature is getting nearer and nearer until, suddenly, too late, the weasel is near enough to make a lightning dash to deliver the fatal bite, usually on the back of its victim's neck.

Among country folk the weasel has the reputation of being fearlessly inquisitive . . . one evening, I spied a tiny bright-eyed head peering at me from behind a tree-trunk. After a few minutes each of us waiting for the other to make the first move, the weasel's curiosity overcame its caution. Slowly, it crept towards me, stopping frequently with one forefoot raised,

ready to flee at the slightest hint of danger. Finally, it arrived to within a whisker's length of my feet. A weasel likes nothing more than a dark hole to investigate and so it was at this moment I remembered the gap between the end of my trouser leg and my shoe. Fearing this 'hole' would prove too much of a temptation, I stooped down and said 'boo'. To my immense relief, it turned and scurried off to disappear in the undergrowth.

Little Owl (*Athene noctua*) OWL FAMILY

Size: The male and female are alike and about the same size 8½ in (22 cm) long.

Breeding: Three to six white, roundish eggs are normally laid between April and May.

The little owl chooses a hole in a tree in which to lay its eggs. Sometimes, however, it will prefer the disused nest of a large bird or even a deserted rabbit burrow. It doesn't bother to make a nest but simply lays the eggs on old food remains.

The hen usually sits on the eggs, which hatch after about 28 days. The baby owls, or owlets, will remain in the nest for a further five weeks before trying out their wings. There is normally one family though occasionally, there may be two. The male shares in the task of rearing the family.

Habits: This plump, flat-headed little owl is more active than most of its larger cousins. It flies from one fence post or similar vantage point to another, seldom remaining still for very long.

Indeed, it is a most excitable little bird and at times will stretch up to its full, tiny height and bob its head up and down in such rapid succession, it almost takes off.

This strange behaviour and the large staring 'eyebrows' certainly give it a very cross appearance.

One evening, my daughter made a little owl very cross indeed. She recorded its voice and immediately played the tape back, whereupon it swooped down from the tree and fearlessly attacked the recording machine in the belief that another owl had invaded its territory.

In flight, its short, rounded wings beat rapidly. When hunting during the day, it adopts an undulating flight, similar to the woodpecker. At dusk, however, it flies in a more direct, purposeful manner.

In common with all owls, the plumage and leading edge of its flight feathers are soft, thus enabling it to fly so silently that its victim is never even aware of its presence.

Although often seen hunting during the day, most of its hunting is done at dawn and dusk. A

bold little hunter, it preys upon birds and mammals, often as large as itself. Much to the pleasure of gardeners and farmers it also has a great fondness for snails, slugs and worms, as well as for reptiles and insects.

The little owl doesn't hoot. Its call is a rather sad high-pitched 'kiew-kiew' often repeated.

Hedgehog *(Erinaceus europaeus)* HEDGEHOG FAMILY

Size: Length about 9–10 in (23–25 cm). Weight up to 2¾ lb (1.25 kg). The female, or sow, is usually smaller than the male, or boar.

Breeding: Two families, or litters, may be born each year sometime between May and September. The nest, or nursery, is usually under a pile of leaves, between the roots of a tree, or in a hole in a bank. This nursery is lined with leaves and moss.

There are normally four or five babies in a litter. They are born blind and their spines are soft. These, however, soon harden and their eyes open when they are about two weeks old. When they are a month old, they leave the nursery and begin to explore their future surroundings. The sow has sole charge of their upbringing and they will remain with her until they are fairly well grown.

Habits: The shape and shambling gait of the hedgehog, or hedgepig, resembles that of a small but spiky badger. It is short sighted and relies on its keen senses of smell and hearing to detect a meal. It sets forth in the evening, grunting, huffing and puffing, nosing its way through the undergrowth to seek out slugs, worms, snails and insects. It will also tuck into frog, mouse, rat, lizard and, being immune to snake poison, snake. Fruit and berries are occasionally eaten but it prefers meat.

The hedgehog is a formidable hunter and, in spite of its short legs, can run quite fast, climb or swim when necessary. If threatened it rolls itself into a spiky ball.

During the coldest part of the winter, it will hibernate in a nest slightly larger than the nursery.

As with most wild creatures who provide a mobile home for all kinds of tiny parasites the hedgehog seems to be favoured by the flea . . . as a student, I

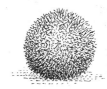

Rolled up and safe inside its own prickly fortress.

found a dead hedgehog which I put into my jacket pocket to take home to study later. I hung my jacket among other family coats on the hall stand.

The following day, my mother, feeling rather uncomfortable in her coat, realised to her horror that she was covered in fleas!

Now I remembered my 'specimen', still waiting to be studied, still in my jacket pocket, still hanging on the hall stand. My mother, on finding all the garments on the stand 'alive', seemed quite upset about the whole affair and banished the hedgehog, the fleas and myself to the garden. The coats were hurriedly burnt.

Wren *(Troglodytes troglodytes)* WREN FAMILY

Size: Length 3¾ in (9.5 cm). The smallest bird found in Britain with the exception of the Goldcrest which is 3½ in (9 cm) long.

Breeding: The male uses grass, leaves and moss to build a nest fairly low down in the hedgerow. The nest is small, neat and dome-shaped with a round side entrance. Occasionally a disused nest of another bird is used.

The male builds several nests for a female to inspect. Should she choose one, she will then proceed to line it with soft feathers.

Some time during April, she will lay about five or six eggs. They are white with fine reddish brown spots. Occasionally though, some eggs are unmarked. The eggs will hatch after about two weeks' incubation and the babies will be ready to fly when about 16 days old. Both parents feed the 'family'.

When food is plentiful, the male may take more than one 'wife' and is kept very busy, endlessly helping to feed his 'families'. A female will normally produce two families a year.

Habits: This delightful, plump little bird with its short, jaunty, upright tail, feels at home in most places. The hedgerow is no exception for it delights in examining every crack and crevice, fallen leaf, twig or stone in its ceaseless search for a succulent insect or spider, which, apart from the occasional seed, form its main diet.

The shy, secretive wren, or Jenny wren as it is sometimes known, is more often heard than seen. The familiar call of 'tic-tic-tic' in a deafeningly loud voice is out of all proportion to its very diminutive size. Another astonishing feat performed by this little bird is its ability to reach up to peck above its head by simply stretching its neck in a quite un-wren-like manner.

The wren, which is with us all the year round, not only performs a service for us by helping to control unwanted insects, but one frequently performs an even more personal service . . . for me!

A tap tap tapping rouses me from my dreams. My little feathered seven o'clock alarm call is working its way along the window putties for its breakfast of the insects that find shelter there. Peering from my pillow, I see the perky little head pause now and then to peer back at me from the other side of my bedroom window before resuming its noisy search. Sleep, under these conditions, is quite impossible.

To Find Out More . . .

To find out more about the birds and mammals in this book, the local library can usually not only recommend books on each subject but can supply addresses of the local wildlife and conservation societies. These societies are always willing to offer help and guidance to anyone wishing to know more about the subject.

In many parts of the country, public footpaths or bridleways may be followed. Their whereabouts may be located through the local public library.

Please remember, fields are seldom open to the public and therefore the owner's permission must always be sought before you enter. If you are granted permission, never walk across the field if it has been planted, walk round the edge and avoid damaging the crop. Also, leave the gate as you find it, if open, leave it open, if closed then close it behind you. Should you need to climb over a gate, always climb over at the 'hinge' end to avoid straining it.

Once in the field, select a spot, preferably in the shade to hide your presence, then sit or lie down and quietly await developments. There is usually a great deal of activity among the hedgerow society which is always fascinating to observe.

Index